The Renaissance
Culture
and the
Arts

By
Jane Pofahl

Illustrated By
Julie Anderson

Cover Illustration By
Mark Anthony

Publishers
T.S. Denison & Company, Inc.
Minneapolis, Minnesota 55431

T.S. Denison and Company, Inc.

Standard Book Number: 513-02195-7
The Renaissance—Culture and the Arts
Copyright © 1993 by T.S. Denison & Co., Inc.
9601 Newton Avenue South
Minneapolis, Minnesota 55431

Introduction

History is the living record of the human race—exciting as it is varied. *The Time Traveler Series* will aid you as you teach the colorful history of the Renaissance and Middle Ages to your children and explore such topics as social structure, medieval government, culture and art forms, scientific discoveries, and the historic personalities who helped shape our own present-day culture.

After each topic is presented, activity pages are provided for your children to implement suggested vocabulary, conduct further research, and provide creative answers/solutions to historical situations. Fun reproducible pages are also included to review the historical and cultural facts studied on the preceding pages.

Each book contains the following:

- topic information pages
- research/activity pages (including maps, charts, research topics, and creative thinking activities)
- reproducible activity pages
- time period stickers

The Time Traveler Series was created to spark the intrigue of your children and lay a foundation for enjoyable history instruction and learning. Have fun!

Table of Contents

The Renaissance

From A.D. 400 into the 1500s, Europeans lived in the Middle Ages. In the early 1300s, a great cultural movement called the Renaissance began in Italy and spread to England, Germany, France, the Netherlands, and Spain. It lasted for approximately three hundred years, but its effects on the world are still felt today.

The Latin-based word "renaissance" means rebirth. During the Middle Ages, Europeans had to work hard just to survive and thus forgot about the arts and teachings from ancient Greece and Rome. Renaissance scholars and artists revived interest in the classical works of the Greeks and Romans. The Renaissance represented a rebirth in art, music, theater, literature, and philosophy.

The leaders of the Renaissance disagreed with many of the attitudes and ideas of people from the Middle Ages, who thought that evil lurked everywhere. During the Renaissance, people began developing their responsibilities to the societies in which they lived. If they took their responsibilities seriously, they could act in a civilized way, not a wicked one.

In the Middle Ages, many people believed that the only important book to study was the Bible. People of the Renaissance still had their religious beliefs, but they expanded their learning into the areas of science, mathematics, law, and philosophy. Major inventions during the Renaissance included the printing press, paper (from cloth), the compass, the astrolabe, the lens, oil painting, gunpowder, sawmills, the spinning wheel, the telescope, and the microscope.

Now, Why Didn't I Think of That?

Many useful and practical inventions were created during the Renaissance. Using the previous information page, choose one of the major inventions of the Renaissance and write its name in the center box. Then write modern day uses for the invention in the surrounding boxes.

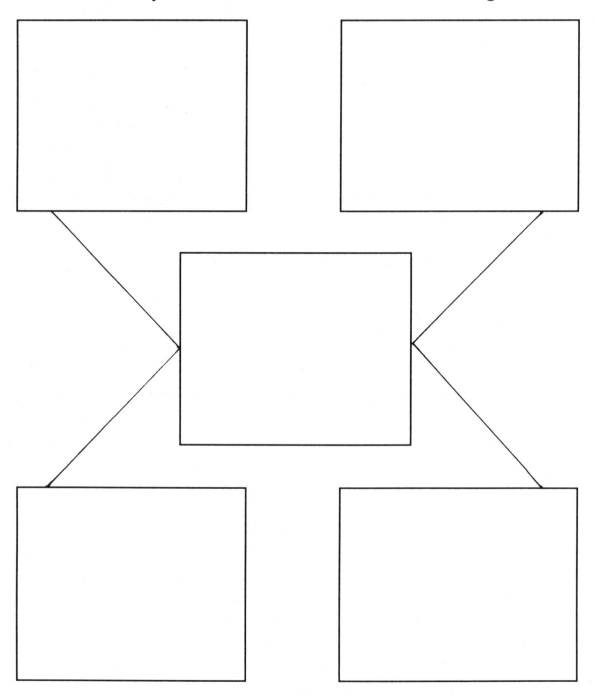

Art

The Renaissance was an age of great art. People were willing to pay large sums of money to acquire objects that would add beauty to their lives.

Middle Age artists painted religious figures in stiff, unnatural poses that were usually symbolic. Renaissance artists, however, wanted to portray the warmth of humanity and used a more lifelike style for their religious artwork.

STATUE BY GHIBERTI

Renaissance sculpture and painting looked more real than the sculpture and painting of the Middle Ages. Michaelangelo and Ghiberti were considered the best sculptors of the Renaissance. Other famous artists during that time included Raphael, Donatello, and Leonardo da Vinci.

Fresco painting was popular in both the Middle Ages and the Renaissance. Artists would paint frescoes, or murals, on walls with tempera paints or water colors. Oil paints were invented in Italy during the Renaissance. Oil paints did not dry as fast as tempera or water colors, so artists could take more time and experiment with colors, textures, and perspective.

Art

RESEARCH QUESTIONS

1. In a dictionary, find the following words: *sum, acquire, pose, symbolic, portray, humanity, fresco, mural, tempera, texture,* and *perspective.* Define each word and use it in a sentence.

2. Find out more about your favorite Renaissance artist. Write a report on an artist such as *Leonardo da Vinci, Michaelangelo, Ghiberti, Donatello, Titian, Raphael, Bellini,* or *Botticelli.* Include illustrations of the artist's work in your report.

3. Architecture is also considered art. Research the life and accomplishments of the master builder of the Renaissance, *Filippo Brunelleschi.*

4. Four artists of the Renaissance, Leonardo da Vinci, Michaelangelo, Donatello, and Raphael, became popular again recently. Why do you think the creator of the *Ninja Turtles* chose Renaissance artists' names?

PROJECTS

1. What is *one-point perspective*? What is *two-point perspective*? Find out and draw examples of each.

2. Make a mobile to commemorate your favorite Renaissance artist. Draw pictures of this artist's work and then suspend the pictures from a wire coat hanger.

3. You can be a sculptor just like Donatello and Michaelangelo! Under the supervision of an adult, carve a bar of soap into a masterpiece.

4. Why did artists have to paint *frescoes* quickly?

Art in Italy

1. Identify the following on your map (refer to a world atlas for a map of Italy):

   - Rome
   - Florence
   - Milan
   - Venice
   - Sicily
   - Corsica
   - Sardinia
   - Mediterranean Sea
   - Tyrrhenian Sea
   - Adriatic Sea

2. Color the water blue and the land tan. Label the Alps and the Apennine Mountains with a series of black X's.
3. Draw a green circle around the city in north central Italy which was ruled for years by the Medici family and was the home of master sculptors Michaelangelo and Ghiberti, as well as painters Raphael and Botticelli.
4. Draw a red triangle around the "canal city" in northeast Italy which inspired the talents of Bellini, Donatello, and Titian.
5. Draw a pink star next to Italy's capital city in west central Italy where works by Raphael and Michaelangelo can still be seen today.
6. Draw a purple box around the extreme northwestern city famous for the La Scala Opera House. The Duke of this city paid Leonardo da Vinci a large sum to create a statue of his father on a horse.

Leonardo da Vinci

Leonardo da Vinci was one of the greatest artists of the Renaissance. In addition to painting, Leonardo studied anatomy, astronomy, botany, and geology. He was also the first to conceptualize the airplane, the submarine, the helicopter, the tank, and the horseless carriage (car).

Leonardo was born in 1452, in the town of Vinci, near Florence, in Italy. During his childhood, Leonardo played in the fields of the family farm and developed a love for nature and animals.

When he was seventeen, Leonardo's father apprenticed him to Verrocchio, a famous painter in Florence. In just three years, Leonardo became a master in the painters' guild.

In 1482, he left Florence to work for the Duke of Milan in Italy. Leonardo used the style of chiaroscuro, or contrasting light and dark paints, while working on his famous painting, *The Last Supper*. He used chiaroscuro in *The Adoration of the Kings* and in his most famous painting, the *Mona Lisa*.

Leonardo was curious about life. He kept sketchbooks filled with drawings of inventions, experiments, interesting people; detailed illustrations of plants and animals; and sketches for sculpture projects. He jumbled his drawings together in no particular order and wrote backwards in mirror-writing to keep his works secret.

Leonardo was paralyzed in 1517. He lived his last two years in a French chateau given to him by King Philip. Leonardo died on May 2, 1519, at the age of sixty-seven.

Leonardo da Vinci

RESEARCH QUESTIONS

1. In a dictionary, find the following words: *anatomy, astronomy, botany, geology, conceptualize, carriage, apprentice, guild, jumble, paralyze,* and *chateau.* Define each word and use it in a sentence.

2. Leonardo worked out his own *cosmology,* or system of the universe. Research the positions of the planets in our universe. Make a chart of the solar system, labeling the planets and writing one fact about each of them in a complete sentence.

3. Leonardo was called the "Renaissance Man." What does the word *renaissance* mean? After reading more about Leonardo, write a one-page paper starting with the words, "Leonardo da Vinci was known as the Renaissance Man because..."

PROJECTS

MONA LISA

1. Leonardo's famous painting of *Mona Lisa* features a woman with a mysterious smile. After looking at a copy of the painting, write what you believe she is thinking.

2. Leonardo became a master of the *chiaroscuro* style, using lights and darks to show depth and dimension. Draw a picture in the chiaroscuro style with black chalk on white paper. Next, draw the same picture with white chalk on black paper and compare the two drawings.

3. Leonardo kept an extensive sketchbook which included designs for his inventions. Find pictures from his sketchbook and copy your favorite drawing of one of his inventions.

4. In order to keep his works secret, Leonardo wrote notes in mirror writing, or backwards writing. Practice writing backwards in either printing or cursive. Write a secret message in mirror writing to a friend.

Leonardo da Vinci Crossword

ACROSS:

3. Leonardo wrote in this way, using a mirror, to keep his works secret.
4. Leonardo served his master, Verrocchio, in this manner.
6. A type of French house where Leonardo spent his last years.
7. A painting by Leonardo showing Jesus Christ and his disciples at a table.
10. Leonardo filled these with drawings and notes.
11. A horseless _____ is another name for an early car.
12. Leonardo worked for the duke of this city in Italy.
13. The most famous Renaissance painter; born in Vinci, Italy.
14. Leonardo earned this honor in the Painters' Guild.

DOWN:

1. Leonardo invented this boat which can carry people underwater.
2. City in Italy where Leonardo learned his painting craft.
5. The style of painting using lights and darks.
8. Time in history in which Leonardo da Vinci lived.
9. The most famous painting by Leonardo da Vinci.

The Medicis

The city of Florence is said to have been the most beautiful city in the world during the Renaissance. Great artists such as Michaelangelo and Raphael lived and worked in Florence under the patronage of the Medici family.

The Medicis were a powerful ruling family in Italy. They made their fortune as bankers and controlled Florence for nearly 140 years.

The first great Medici was Giovanni de Medici (1360–1429). Through trading and banking, he started the Medici dynasty.

Cosimo de Medici (1389–1464) was Giovanni's son. He gave large amounts of money to promote the arts in Florence. Cosimo was known as the Father of His Country.

The most famous Medici of all was Lorenzo the Magnificent (1449–1492), who was the grandson of Cosimo. Under his influence, Florence became the most powerful city-state in Italy. Lorenzo built beautiful buildings and established libraries throughout the area.

Two women of the Medici family became queens of France. Catherine de Medici married Henry II and was the mother of three French kings. Marie de Medici married Henry IV. After he died, she ruled France until their son, Louis XIII, was old enough to take over.

The Medicis

RESEARCH QUESTIONS

1. In a dictionary, find the following words: *patronage, fortune, dynasty, promote, influence, city-state,* and *establish.* Define each word and use it in a sentence.

2. Find out more about the most famous Medici ruler, *Lorenzo the Magnificent.* What did he do to receive that name? Did he have any children? How did he die? Present your findings in a report.

3. The two Medici sisters, Catherine and Maria, married French kings. Choose one of the two sisters and research her life. Compile your findings with others in your class who chose the same person and present your information as a group to the rest of the class.

·LORENZO THE MAGNIFICENT·

THE STATUE OF DAVID

PROJECTS

1. The Medicis made the city of Florence one of the most beautiful cities in the world. Find pictures and maps of Florence during the Renaissance. Draw the city of Florence.

2. Michaelangelo's famous statue, *David*, was commissioned, or paid for, by Lorenzo Medici to symbolize the city of Florence. Design a statue to stand for the spirit of your city.

3. Lorenzo the Magnificent started the first public libraries in Italy. Design an advertisement for the local Florence newspaper announcing the opening festivities for the new library.

Marking Time with the Medicis

The Medici family were powerful rulers in Italy during the Renaissance. They controlled the banking and almost everything else in Florence for approximately 140 years.

Using the information page, make a timeline for the amazing Medicis. Locate the birth and death of each of the following Medici rulers on the timeline:

> Giovanni de Medici
> Cosimo de Medici
> Lorenzo de Medici

In addition to these rulers, locate the birth and death of each of the Medici queens of France on the timeline:

> **Catherine de Medici 1519–1589**
> **Marie de Medici 1573–1642**

1300   1350   1400   1450   1500   1550   1600   1650   1700

Michaelangelo

When Michaelangelo was born on March 6, 1475, near Florence, Italy, his father thought he saw lucky signs in the sky. He named his child Michaelangelo, because the Italian word *angelo* in Italian means angel.

Michaelangelo drew and painted constantly as a boy. His father and uncles tried to interest him in law and politics, but Michaelangelo was determined to be an artist. Reluctantly, his father apprenticed him at age thirteen to a master painter in Florence.

In the workshop, Michaelangelo learned to paint frescoes, or murals usually painted on wet plaster. Soon he became an assistant to the master painter, but the other apprentices disliked him for his quick temper; his criticism of their work; and his talent, which was far beyond their own skills.

When he was sixteen, Michaelangelo met Lorenzo de Medici, who became a patron for Michaelangelo. Under Lorenzo's guidance, Michaelangelo studied Greek sculpture and anatomy to understand human muscle and bone structure.

Michaelangelo created many works of beauty that exist today. Famous statues by Michaelangelo include the *Pieta*, *David*, and *Moses*. He worked for forty years sculpting the figures on Pope Julius's burial tomb. His most famous masterpiece is his painting that covers the entire ceiling of the Sistene Chapel in Rome. He was also the chief architect for St. Peter's Basilica in Rome.

Michaelangelo died a very famous man on February 18, 1564, in Rome.

Michaelangelo

ADAM'S CREATION
FROM THE CEILING OF THE SISTINE CHAPEL

RESEARCH QUESTIONS

1. In a dictionary, find the following words: *constantly, politics, determined, reluctantly, criticism, patron, guidance, anatomy, exist, basilica,* and *architect.* Define each word and use it in a sentence.

2. Find out more about the master Renaissance artist Michaelangelo. Did he have a last name? What was his favorite medium—paint or marble? Present your findings in a written report.

3. Research Michaelangelo's accomplishments in sculpture, painting, and architecture. Draw and label examples of his finest works and compile them in a Michaelangelo scrapbook.

PROJECTS

1. One of Michaelangelo's greatest achievements was painting a huge mural of Bible stories on the ceiling of the Sistene Chapel in Rome. In a cooperative learning group, work with others in your class to create a mural about Renaissance times.

2. When he was a young man, Michaelangelo criticized the work of fellow artist Pietro Torrigiano, who in turn broke Michaelangelo's nose and scarred his face. How could Pietro have acted differently? How could Michaelangelo have acted differently? Was either right? If so, why?

3. Michaelangelo was a perfectionist. It took him four years to paint the Sistine Chapel because he did not trust any one else to help him paint it. List things in your life that you would rather do by yourself so that you know they would be done right.

4. Look at a photo of the *Pieta* sculpture by Michaelangelo. Notice how young Mary looks. Why would Michaelangelo choose to portray her as a young woman in this sculpture?

Michaelangelo's Sculpture Class

This is the moment you have been waiting for! Your teacher, master sculptor Michaelangelo, just gave you your final assignment in your formal training as a sculptor. You must create your masterpiece sculpture from a block of stone. The first step is, of course, to plan your design for the sculpture. In the space below, draw a sketch for your masterpiece. Make it as perfect a drawing as you can, including every detail. Remember, the master is watching you!

Printing

Historians agree that the most important development during the Renaissance was the printing press with moveable type that Johannes Gutenberg invented in Germany in 1444.

Gutenberg perfected his idea of casting, or forming individual letters in metal. He arranged the letters into words and then fit them into a wooden frame. Black ink was brushed on to the metal letters. He then took a large white sheet of paper and pressed it firmly on top of the letters. When he carefully peeled the paper off of the letters, Gutenberg had an entire page of typeset printing. To print another page, he cleaned the metal letters, arranged them into new words, and repeated the process.

The printing press with movable type revolutionized learning. Before this time, books were written by hand and were very expensive. Only the wealthy could afford to buy books. Now, multiple books could be produced in a short amount of time. The price of books dropped so that farmers as well as nobles could afford to buy them—an interest in reading and learning had been revived.

Once people found that books could be mass-produced, maps and atlases were also printed on the press. Navigators and explorers had more up-to-date, accurate maps as they sailed across the oceans to explore the New World.

Printing

RESEARCH QUESTIONS

1. In a dictionary, find the following words: *historian, casting, revolutionize, afford, multiple, noble, mass-produce, atlas, navigator,* and *accurate.* Define each word and use it in a sentence.

2. Find out more about Johannes Gutenberg. When and where was he born? How did he come to invent movable type? Did he have any children? Give a presentation on Johannes Gutenberg to the class using pictures, maps, and visual aids.

3. Research the history of *paper making.* Who invented paper? How has it changed through the years? Write a report on paper making.

4. How did people make books before printing was invented? Research the history of books and printing presses. Report your findings to the class.

PROJECTS

1. Make a crossword puzzle (and an answer key!) about Johannes Gutenberg and his printing press.

2. Make a potato press. With the help of an adult, cut a potato in half with a sharp knife. Draw a simple design on the flat half of the potato (such as a heart or square). Cut away the potato around the design about 1/4" so that your design is raised from the rest of the flat potato. Dip the design into tempera paint and press the potato design to the paper. You now have your own designer stationery!

Start the Presses!

How did Johannes Gutenberg make the first printing press with movable type? To find out, put the following steps in their correct order from 1 to 7.

_____ Then he took a large piece of white paper and pressed it firmly on top of the letters.

_____ When the metal letters were formed, he arranged them into words.

_____ To print a different page, Johannes changed the letters and repeated the process.

_____ Then Johannes placed the metal words into a wooden frame.

_____ He brushed black ink on the metal letters.

_____ First, Johannes Gutenberg cast individual letters in metal.

_____ When he peeled the paper off the letters, he had a page of typeset printing.

Music

During the Middle Ages, most of the music people heard was composed for church services. Sometimes an entire mass, or service, was sung rather than spoken. The same melody, called *cantus firmus*, was used throughout the service.

The Renaissance brought a rebirth to music as well. Musicians wrote sacred music to glorify God in a different way than before. Composers developed the polyphonic style in which all four voices—soprano, alto, tenor, and bass—had melody lines. No one voice was more important than the others. Palestrina was a master of polyphonic sacred music. Gabrieli also wrote sacred music that has survived time.

Musicians began writing secular music as well. Also known as popular music, these songs told of brave deeds, described a lover, or mourned a lost love. These songs were called chansons, from the French word meaning "songs." Clement Janequin was know for his witty chansons.

In the 1500s, the madrigal style became popular in Italy and England. Madrigals also were about love, but they were more sophisticated than the chanson. In Italy, the leading madrigal composer was Monteverdi. The English favored Thomas Morley's madrigals.

Renaissance musicians used instruments as well as voices to make music. The harpsichord was popular, as were flutes, oboes, guitars, and hand drums.

Music

RESEARCH QUESTIONS

1. In a dictionary, find the following words: *compose, mass, melody, sacred, glorify, secular, deed, mourn, witty, madrigal, sophisticated,* and *harpsichord.* Define each word and use it in a sentence.

2. Many important composers lived during the Renaissance. Find out more about the life and work of *Palestrina, Gabrieli, Monteverdi, Clement Janequin,* or *Thomas Morley.* Record your findings in a report.

3. *Opera* began in the late 1590s in Florence, Italy. Research the history of opera by finding recordings of operas from the 1600s to the present. Put the recordings in chronological order and introduce and play examples of them for the class.

PROJECTS

1. Choose your favorite Renaissance instrument and make it yourself. Play it for the class.

2. Write the lyrics to your own *chanson.* You could write above the brave deeds of a hero, describe a romance, or lament a lost love.

3. Make a collage of Renaissance instruments. Look in books to find out what the instruments looked like, then draw them on your paper in an interesting design.

4. Listen to a piece of Renaissance music by any of the composers mentioned in the reading. Write a story to accompany the music. If you wish, illustrate your story.

Theatre

People went to the theater during the Renaissance for the same reasons people go to the movies today—to laugh, relax, and escape from their own cares for a while. The price of a theater ticket was very affordable (sometimes free), so everyone from a peasant to a king could enjoy a day at the theater.

In Italy, a popular style of theater was called commedia dell'arte. Actors improvised their words and actions around a basic storyline. The plot was usually a funny story about young people in love outwitting their parents or guardians.

Queen Elizabeth I in England was a great patron of the arts. She supported the most famous playwright of all time, William Shakespeare. Believing that theater could be both entertaining and educational, he wrote plays produced in public theaters for people from all classes.

The most well-known theater in London was called the Globe Theatre. Shakespeare's Globe was an open-air theater where poorer theatergoers could stand in front of the stage to watch a show, and wealthier patrons could pay more to sit on benches high up in the gallery.

Very little scenery was used in Elizabethan theater, but actors wore lavish costumes and used many props, such as swords and scepters. No women were allowed to perform on the stage. Boys played the roles of women and children. By today's standards, Elizabethan theater might be considered amateurish, but it was extremely popular entertainment in the 1500s.

Theater

RESEARCH QUESTIONS

1. In a dictionary, find the following words: *affordable, peasant, commedia dell' arte, plot, improvise, outwit, guardian, patron, playwright, gallery, lavish, prop, scepter, standard,* and *amateur.* Define each word and use it in a sentence.

2. The most popular style of theater in Italy during the Renaissance was *commedia dell'arte.* Research the history of commedia dell'arte. Inform the class of your findings in a presentation.

3. Find out more about the *Globe Theatre.* When was it built? Who owned it? What kind of entertainment was performed there? What did it look like? Write your findings in a report and include a drawing of the Globe Theatre.

PROJECTS

1. Create your own version of commedia dell'arte. Decide what your basic plot will be. Assign roles to actors and actresses and have fun improvising your dialogue!

2. The Globe Theatre was the most popular and famous theater in London, England, during the Renaissance. Make a model of the Globe.

3. Read a *synopsis,* or summary, of a play by Shakespeare. Retell the story using your own words and drawings to follow the plot.

4. Be an audience! Attend a play in your area.

The Play's the Thing

The great Bard of Avon himself, William Shakespeare, has graced you with his presence in your printing shop. He asks you, the finest poster artist in all of London, to design a poster for any one of his plays for display in the lobby of the Globe Theatre. His only requirement is that you write the name of the play (and his name as the playwright, of course) clearly on the poster. You may use any color scheme and illustrations you choose to make the play come alive in the minds of the theatre patrons. You know that many people attend plays at the Globe and that this is a golden opportunity to advertise your poster designs, so you do your best work.

- Choose a play by Shakespeare.

- In the space below, draw out the design for your poster.

- After you have your poster planned, get a sheet of white construction paper from your teacher.

- Draw the design for your poster and color it using any of the following:
  - crayons
  - colored pencils
  - markers
  - tempera paint, brushes, and water
  - chalk
  - construction paper and glue

- Display your Shakespeare play poster in your classroom.

Clothing

The Renaissance was a time to celebrate life by wearing brightly colored, loose-fitting clothes. Both men and women dressed extravagantly in silks, brocades, and laces. Belts and buckles with ornate designs were in high demand. Jewelry, such as rings, necklaces, and bracelets were popular as well.

The well-dressed man wore a small cap and a very short low-cut jacket that was laced over a soft low-cut shirt. He wore multicolored tights and soft shoes. Older men wore long gowns with full sleeves.

Women wore simple, high-waisted gowns with sleeves tied at the wrist and laced to the arms. They wore slipper-like shoes on their feet. Women either braided their hair or wore a garland of flowers.

Wigs were popular during the Renaissance. Peasant women would grow their hair long in order to cut it off and sell it. The most popular hair color was blonde, and like today, both men and women dyed their hair. High foreheads were considered very fashionable, so women often shaved their hairline back on their foreheads. Wealthy women polished their nails and used make-up on their faces and eyelids.

Perfumes and incense were used heavily to cover up unpleasant odors. People carried perfumed handkerchiefs and small perfume bottles as pendants on necklaces. Perfume was even rubbed into animals. Perfumes such as peppermint and cinnamon were added to bath water. People only took baths every few weeks, so they needed to wear heavy perfumes!

Clothing

RESEARCH QUESTIONS

1. In a dictionary, find the following words: *extravagant, brocade, ornate, multicolored, garland, dye, incense,* and *pendant.* Define each word and use it in a sentence.

2. Find out more about Renaissance clothing. Research what a wealthy person and a peasant would have worn. Draw examples of each.

3. Find pictures of Renaissance clothing styles from England, Italy, France, and Spain. On a chart, draw an example of clothing from each country and write a description of the differences between them.

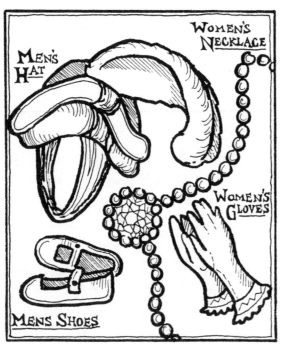

PROJECTS

1. Make a Renaissance Fashion Book for men, women, or children. Include detailed sketches of items such as undergarments, stockings, shoes, gloves, hats, jewelry, and purses or pouches.

2. Design a piece of jewelry to be presented to the queen on her next birthday. (She loves gold and jewels such as rubies, sapphires, amethysts, and emeralds.)

3. Find pictures of Renaissance headwear and then make a similar hat out of any materials you have available.

4. Hold a Renaissance Fashion Show. Include clothing worn by peasants, craftsmen, merchants, clergy, and nobles and their ladies.

Leisure Activities

People of the Renaissance enjoyed life and put energy and enthusiasm into their games and sports. Children were encouraged to play and use their imaginations with dolls, toy boats, mud pies, and marbles.

After the weather turned cold and ice covered the rivers, people of the Renaissance strapped iron blades to their shoes and skated. When it snowed, they tied the thigh bones of animals to their feet and used iron-tipped poles to ski.

People living in the Renaissance also enjoyed indoor games. Chess was popular with both men and women. Checkers, card games, and an early version of backgammon helped people pass the time on dreary winter nights.

Storytellers were in high demand as entertainment after banquets. Dance masters taught the daughters of nobles to dance gracefully at balls. The most popular dance was the galliard. Parties, dances, and balls were well-attended during the Renaissance.

Singers, dancers, and actors were hired to entertain at parties and celebrations. Masques and mummeries were plays in which the actors wore masks. Singers entertained noble guests with madrigals, or four-voice songs. Opera was also popular in Italy at this time.

Leisure Activities

RESEARCH QUESTIONS

1. In a dictionary, find the following words: *enthusiasm, encourage, thigh, version, dreary, ball, galliard, hired, masque, mummery,* and *opera.* Define each word and use it in a sentence.

2. Find out more about *masques* and *mummeries.* Who took part in a masque? What happened at such an event? Write your findings in a report.

3. The word *carnival* brings to mind bright lights, music, mechanical rides, lots of balloons, and cotton candy. Locate the original meaning of "carnival" and report your findings to the group.

MUMMERY MASK

PROJECTS

1. The most popular dance of the Renaissance was the simple, yet elegant, *galliard.* Learn how to dance the galliard and then teach it to a friend.

2. Fairy tales originated during medieval times in Europe. Create your own fairy tale. Remember to include a likeable hero or heroine, a problem to solve, and a mean villain.

3. Make a garland wreath for your hair. Cover a thin wire with hair ribbon and wrap dried baby's breath flowers around the covered wire. Weave dried flowers into the baby's breath.

4. Make a toy pinwheel. Glue two different colored 4" paper squares together. Cut slits from each corner. Fold the corners in (see diagram). Push a pin through the tips of the folded sections, through the back, and then into the stick. Blow on the pinwheel or let the wind spin it around.

HOW TO MAKE A PINWHEEL

The Renaissance Game

During the Renaissance, people loved to pass time playing games of all kinds. Board games, card games, games of chance, and party games were among the favorite hobbies of medieval monarchs, as well as poor peasants.

You can create your own Renaissance game. You will need:

- tagboard
- pencils and pens
- markers
- buttons to use as gameboard tokens
- construction paper (optional)
- glue (optional)

1. The first thing you need to do is to make your gameboard. For ideas, look at the boards from games such as *Sorry!*, *Life*, *Candyland*, or *Monopoly*.

2. Next, you will need to make cards that give various directions: "You fell into the moat—lose 1 turn." or "Hurray! You won the king's jousting tournament. Move ahead 2 spaces." You may choose to write the directions in the gameboard squares instead.

3. To decide who goes first and how many spaces to move, use dice or make your own spinner out of tagboard, markers, and a brad. (Laminate for durability.)

4. Once you have made your Renaissance game, find at least one other person and play it!

Renaissance Timeline

1300	Renaissance begins.
1360–1429	Giovanni de Medici (A wealthy banker in Florence, Italy.)
1389–1464	Cosimo de Medici ("The Father of His Country")
1444	Johannes Gutenberg uses movable type in a printing press.
1482	Leonardo da Vinci worked for the Duke of Milan in Italy and painted *The Last Supper*.
1449–1492	Lorenzo de Medici (Lorenzo the Magnificent)
1500s	Madrigal style of music popular in Italy and France.
1559–1603	Elizabeth I rules England.
1564	Michaelangelo died in Rome.
1595	William Shakespeare wrote plays performed at the Globe Theatre in London, England.
1600s	Renaissance ends.

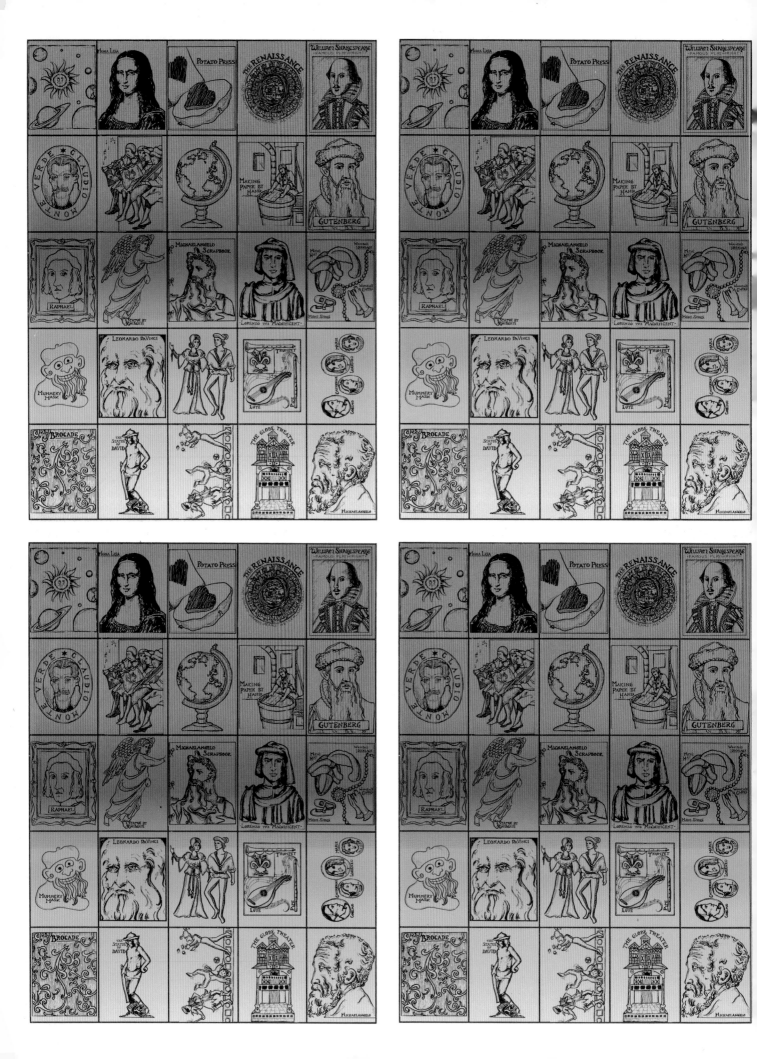